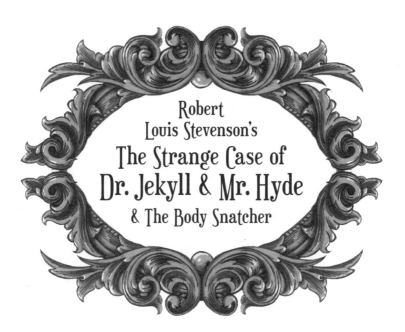

Robert
Louis Stevenson's
The Strange Case of
Dr. Jekyll & Mr. Hyde
& The Body Snatcher

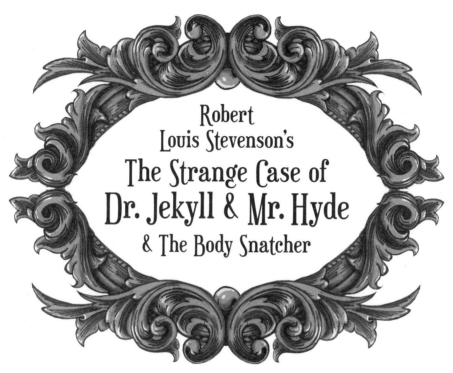

Robert
Louis Stevenson's
The Strange Case of
Dr. Jekyll & Mr. Hyde
& The Body Snatcher

A Graphic Novel

ILLUSTRATED BY ROBERT SMITH

METRO BOOKS
New York

Dedicated to Jess, my family,
and friends, for putting up with me
when I'm more Hyde than Jekyll

METRO BOOKS
New York

An Imprint of Sterling Publishing
1166 Avenue of the Americas
New York, NY 10036

Conceived, designed, and produced by
Quid Publishing
Level 4 Sheridan House
114 Western Road
Hove BN3 1DD
England
Illustrations by Robert Smith
The Strange Case of Dr. Jekyll and Mr. Hyde script by Lucy York
"The Body Snatcher" script by Sarah Herman

www.quidpublishing.com

ISBN 978-1-4351-6153-5

For information about custom editions, special sales, and premium and corporate purchases, please contact Sterling Special Sales at 800-805-5489 or specialsales@sterlingpublishing.com.

Manufactured in China

2 4 6 8 10 9 7 5 3 1

www.sterlingpublishing.com

Contents

Introduction

The Strange Case of Dr. Jekyll and Mr. Hyde by Robert Louis Stevenson (1850–1894) was first published in 1886 as a "shilling shocker," a creepy tale sold in paperback format for one shilling, intended to give its mass market readers a "pleasurable chill." The novella has since become one of the most famous horror stories of all time, adapted into films, TV series, and stage productions. It famously tackles the concept of the split personality and the conflict between good and evil within the human psyche. To this very day, the phrase "a Jekyll and Hyde character" is used to describe someone who outwardly seems good but has a secret dark side.

Stevenson's father intended for his son to go into the family civil engineering business, but Stevenson had other ideas. He first pursued a law degree at Edinburgh University, then after being diagnosed with a severe respiratory illness decided to become a professional writer. *Jekyll and Hyde* was his first real commercial success, affording him financial independence. Anecdote would have it that the first transformation scene came to Stevenson in a dream, and that he completed the novella in just three days.

When creating the artwork for *The Strange Case of Dr. Jekyll and Mr. Hyde*, one of the biggest challenges was how to realize Hyde, one of the most iconic horror characters of all time. The idea was to have Hyde's nastiness escalate as the frequency of potion doses increases, going from initially just mischievous to eventually downright murderous. When I drew the initial character study for Hyde I had in my mind the sort of bad guys that you are drawn to and want to see more of: antiheroes like the Joker, the Mask (from the graphic novel), Captain Jack Sparrow, and Tuco from *The Good, The Bad and the Ugly*. I wanted him to be roguish but also dangerous and unpredictable, rather than a full-on mutant. The transformation was to be more of a mental one than a physical one—even though his looks change significantly, it's important to remember that he is still human, and essentially an extension of Dr. Jekyll's bad side.

Another important consideration was how to create a believable world in which the action would take place. I used 3D-animation techniques to build a virtual "set" for Jekyll's house, which helped me to keep the layout consistent and also allowed me to better visualize the action from different angles. For artistic inspiration, I looked to Mike Mignola, Dave Stewart, and Craig Thompson.

As *Jekyll and Hyde* is only a novella, we also had room in this edition to include Stevenson's short story "The Body Snatcher," a fictionalized account of the very real Mr. Burke and Mr. Hare, two infamous grave-robbers who operated in Edinburgh in 1828. I hope you will enjoy reading both stories, and that they will give you the "pleasurable chill" that Stevenson originally intended.

Dramatis Personae

The Strange Case of Dr. Jekyll and Mr. Hyde

MR. HYDE

DR. JEKYLL

MR. UTTERSON

MR. ENFIELD

DR. LANYON

MR. POOLE

SIR CAREW

DETECTIVE
NEWCOMEN

MR. UTTERSON'S
MAID

The Body Snatcher

MR. FETTES

MR. MACFARLANE

THE LANDLORD

JANE GALBRAITH

MR. GRAY

Chapter One

THE ESTEEMED DR. JEKYLL WAS HOSTING ONE OF HIS FAMOUS DINNER PARTIES AT HIS HOME IN LONDON...

MAY I RAISE A TOAST, GENTLEMEN...

... TO THE OLDEST OF FRIENDS...

... AND TO FRIENDS NEW.

TO FRIENDS OLD AND NEW!

THANK YOU FOR A WONDERFUL EVENING.

AND DON'T TAKE HIS WORDS TO HEART, WILL YOU?

HE'S A STUBBORN OLD TRADITIONALIST, YOU KNOW.

THANK YOU, UTTERSON.

AT LAST, I CAN RELAX!

OH, THE PROFOUND DUPLICITY OF MY EXISTENCE...

TO BE PREDISPOSED TO ENJOY SOME OF LIFE'S GUILTY PLEASURES...

... AND YET TO FEEL *COMPELLED* TO PRESENT MYSELF TO SOCIETY AS AN UPSTANDING, IMMACULATE CITIZEN.

THEY MOCK, BUT THEY DO NOT KNOW WHAT I KNOW...

... THAT MAN IS NOT TRULY *ONE*...

Chapter Two

IT WAS A SUNDAY AFTERNOON, AND MR. UTTERSON AND HIS OLD FRIEND MR. RICHARD ENFIELD WERE OUT FOR THEIR HABITUAL WALK AROUND LONDON WHEN THEY CAME UPON A STRANGE DOOR.

HAVE YOU EVER NOTICED THAT DOOR?

WHY, YES, I HAVE.

IT IS CONNECTED IN MY MIND WITH A VERY ODD STORY.

INDEED? AND WHAT WAS THAT?

WELL, I WAS COMING HOME FROM SOME PLACE AT THE END OF THE WORLD, ABOUT THREE O'CLOCK ON A BLACK WINTER MORNING...

... IT WAS A DESERTED PART OF TOWN, WITH NOTHING TO SEE BUT LAMPS...

... ALL AT ONCE, I SAW TWO FIGURES, A SHORT MAN CHARGING ALONG ONE STREET, AND A LITTLE GIRL RUNNING DOWN THE STREET TOWARD ME.

OF COURSE...

...THEY RAN INTO EACH OTHER AT THE CORNER...

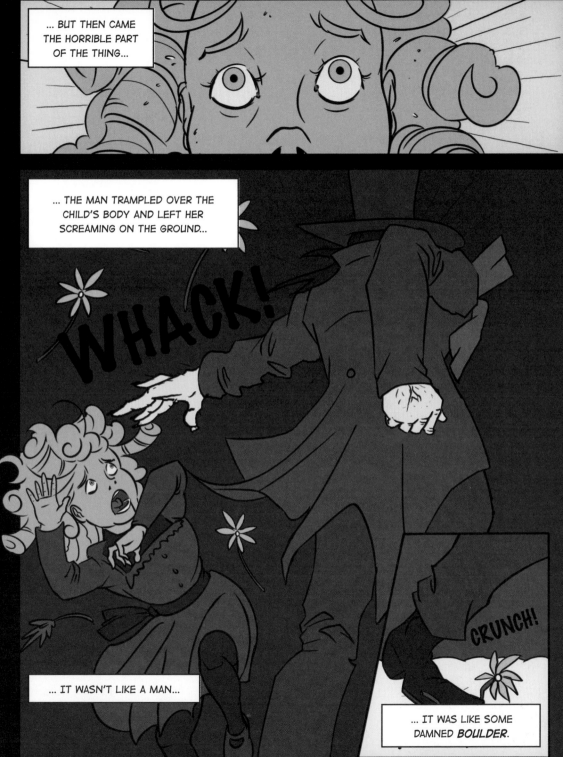

Chapter Three

CAME HOME TO HIS BACHELOR HOUSE IN SOMBER SPIRITS.

LONG HAS THIS DOCUMENT BEEN MY EYESORE...

Last Will & Testament

In the case of the decease of Henry Jekyll, all of his possessions are to pass into the hands of his friend and benefactor Edward Hyde, but that in the case of Henry Jekyll's disappearance or unexplained absence for any period exceeding three calendar months, the said Edward Hyde should step into the said Henry Jekyll's shoes without further delay.

... IT OFFENDS ME BOTH AS A LAWYER AND A LOVER OF THE SANE AND CUSTOMARY SIDES OF LIFE...

... NOW THE NAME HYDE HAS BEEN CLOTHED IN DETESTABLE ATTRIBUTES...

... I THOUGHT IT WAS MADNESS AND NOW I BEGIN TO FEAR IT IS DISGRACE...

... IF ANYONE CAN HELP ME GET TO THE BOTTOM OF THIS, IT'S LANYON.

UTTERSON MADE HASTE TO LANYON'S HOUSE.

I SUPPOSE, LANYON, YOU AND I MUST BE THE TWO OLDEST FRIENDS THAT HENRY JEKYLL HAS?

I SUPPOSE WE ARE. I SEE LITTLE OF HIM NOW.

INDEED? I THOUGHT YOU HAD A BOND OF COMMON INTEREST.

WE HAD. BUT IT IS MORE THAN TEN YEARS SINCE HENRY JEKYLL BECAME TOO FANCIFUL FOR ME. HE BEGAN TO GO WRONG, WRONG IN MIND. SUCH UNSCIENTIFIC BALDERDASH!

THEY HAVE ONLY DIFFERED ON SOME POINT OF SCIENCE, IT IS NOTHING WORSE THAN THAT.

DID YOU EVER COME ACROSS A PROTEGE OF HIS--ONE HYDE?

HYDE? NO, NEVER HEARD OF HIM.

NONE THE WISER, THE TROUBLED UTTERSON WENT HOME AND RETIRED FOR THE NIGHT.

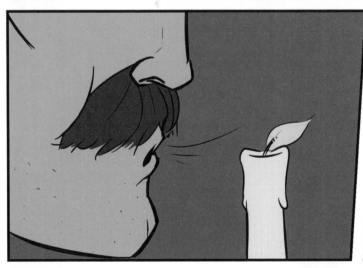

THAT NIGHT, A FACELESS MR. HYDE HAUNTED HIS NIGHTMARES.

THE NEXT DAY, MR. UTTERSON ROSE DETERMINED TO SOLVE THE MYSTERY OF THE ELUSIVE MR. HYDE.

IF HE BE MR. HYDE...

... I SHALL BE MR. SEEK.

BONG!

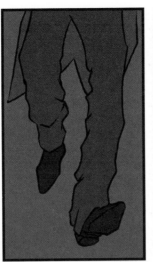

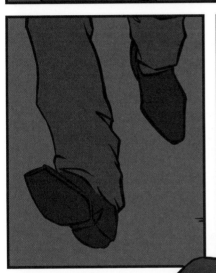

MR. HYDE, I THINK?

THAT IS MY NAME. WHAT DO YOU WANT?

NOW I SHALL KNOW YOU AGAIN. IT MAY BE USEFUL.

IT IS GOOD WE HAVE MET. HERE, YOU MAY AS WELL HAVE MY ADDRESS. I DON'T LIVE AROUND HERE; I LIVE IN SOHO.

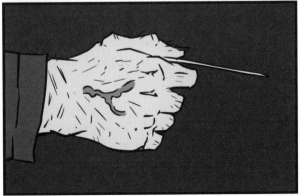

UNSETTLED BY THE ENCOUNTER, MR. UTTERSON MADE HIS WAY ROUND TO DR. JEKYLL'S FRONT DOOR TO INVESTIGATE FURTHER.

KNOCK! KNOCK!

IS DR. JEKYLL AT HOME, POOLE?

I AM AFRAID HE IS OUT, MR. UTTERSON. WILL YOU COME IN AND WARM YOURSELF BY THE FIRE, SIR?

I SAW MR. HYDE GO IN BY THE OLD LABORATORY DOOR, POOLE. IS THAT RIGHT, WHEN DR. JEKYLL ISN'T AT HOME?

QUITE RIGHT, MR. UTTERSON, SIR. MR. HYDE HAS A KEY.

YOUR MASTER SEEMS TO HAVE A GREAT DEAL OF TRUST IN THAT YOUNG MAN.

WELL, GOOD NIGHT, POOLE.

YES, SIR, HE DOES INDEED. WE ALL HAVE ORDERS TO OBEY HIM. BUT WE SEE VERY LITTLE OF HIM THIS SIDE OF THE HOUSE. HE MOSTLY COMES AND GOES BY THE LABORATORY.

GOOD NIGHT, MR. UTTERSON.

POOR HARRY JEKYLL! SOMETHING TELLS ME HE IS IN DEEP WATERS! HE WAS WILD WHEN HE WAS YOUNG.

IT MUST BE THE GHOST OF SOME OLD SIN, THE CANCER OF SOME CONCEALED DISGRACE.

THIS MASTER HYDE, IF HE WERE STUDIED, MUST HAVE SOME SECRETS OF HIS OWN; DARK SECRETS, BY THE LOOK OF HIM. THINGS CANNOT CONTINUE AS THEY ARE. IF THIS HYDE SUSPECTS THE EXISTENCE OF THE WILL, HE MAY GROW IMPATIENT TO INHERIT! I MUST GET TO THE BOTTOM OF THIS.

Chapter Four

A FORTNIGHT LATER, BY EXCELLENT GOOD FORTUNE, THE DOCTOR GAVE ANOTHER ONE OF HIS PLEASANT DINNERS. AS WAS OFTEN HIS HABIT, UTTERSON REMAINED AFTER THE OTHER GUESTS HAD LEFT TO CONVERSE WITH DR. JEKYLL.

I HAVE BEEN WANTING TO SPEAK TO YOU, JEKYLL. YOU KNOW THAT *WILL* OF YOURS?

MY POOR UTTERSON, YOU ARE UNFORTUNATE IN SUCH A CLIENT.

I NEVER SAW A MAN SO DISTRESSED AS YOU WERE BY MY WILL, OTHER THAN THAT HIDE-BOUND PEDANT, LANYON.

YOU KNOW I NEVER APPROVED OF IT.

MY WILL? YES, CERTAINLY, I KNOW THAT. YOU HAVE TOLD ME SO.

WELL, I TELL YOU SO AGAIN. I HAVE BEEN LEARNING SOMETHING OF YOUNG *HYDE*.

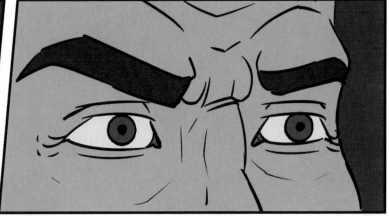

I DO NOT CARE TO HEAR MORE. THIS IS A MATTER I THOUGHT WE'D AGREED TO DROP.

WHAT I HEARD WAS ABOMINABLE.

THAT DOESN'T CHANGE ANYTHING. YOU DO NOT UNDERSTAND MY POSITION. I AM PAINFULLY SITUATED, UTTERSON.

I AM YOUR FRIEND AND A MAN TO BE TRUSTED. COME CLEAN ABOUT THIS IN CONFIDENCE AND I MAKE NO DOUBT I CAN GET YOU OUT OF IT.

I BELIEVE YOU FULLY. I WOULD TRUST YOU BEFORE ANY MAN ALIVE. BUT IT ISN'T WHAT YOU FANCY...

... JUST TO PUT YOUR GOOD HEART AT REST, I WILL TELL YOU ONE THING...

... THE MOMENT I CHOOSE, I CAN BE RID OF MR. HYDE...

... THIS IS A PRIVATE MATTER, AND I BEG OF YOU TO LET IT SLEEP.

I HAVE NO DOUBT YOU ARE PERFECTLY RIGHT.

ONE FURTHER THING. I KNOW YOU HAVE SEEN HYDE--HE TOLD ME SO--AND I FEAR HE WAS RUDE. BUT I DO SINCERELY TAKE A GREAT, A VERY GREAT INTEREST IN THAT YOUNG MAN...

... IF I AM TAKEN AWAY I WISH YOU TO PROMISE ME THAT YOU WILL GET HIS RIGHTS FOR HIM.

WELL, I PROMISE.

YES, I CAN BE RID OF HYDE WHENEVER I CHOOSE... BUT THAT TIME HASN'T COME QUITE YET...

... AFTER ALL...

... IT IS ONLY TO INDULGE MY PLEASURES WITHOUT CENSURE THAT I SEEK HIS DISGUISE.

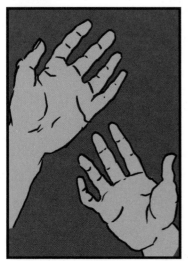

HE VISITED THE MOST DISREPUTABLE OF DRINKING ESTABLISHMENTS...

...AND DRANK TO EXCESS.

YOU MIGHT AS WELL LEAVE ME THE BOTTLE.

WHAT ARE
YOU TWO LOOKING
AT?!

59

GROWN TIRED OF DRINKING AND VIOLENCE, HE
WENT IN SEARCH OF YET DEEPER INTOXICATIONS...

AH SINGS

STEP THIS
WAY, SIR.

EVERYTHING YOU NEED TO RELAX IS HERE...

AFTER HIS ESCAPADES, HE WOULD RETURN UNNOTICED TO THE LABORATORY, WHERE HE WOULD DRINK THE ANTIDOTE AND REVERT TO JEKYLL. THAT IS, UNTIL ONE MORNING, WHEN TO HIS HORROR HE AWOKE STILL IN HIS GHASTLY GUISE AT HYDE'S APARTMENT IN SOHO...

I AM SLOWLY LOSING HOLD OF MY ORIGINAL AND BETTER SELF, AND BECOMING INCORPORATED WITH MY SECOND AND WORSE...

Chapter Five

GOOD EVENING, SIR!

WHACK!

MR. UTTERSON, SIR, YOU MUST COME... SOMETHING *TERRIBLE* HAS HAPPENED!

WHATEVER IS THE MATTER? WOULD YOU BE SO KIND AS TO WAIT WHILE I *DRESS*?

WE ARE TOO *LATE*. HE IS QUITE DEAD.

LOOK, SIR...

MUST BE BECAUSE HE BEAT HIM SO H--

... IT'S BROKEN...

SHUSH, NOW. RUN AND CALL FOR THE POLICE.

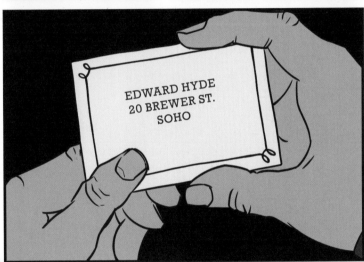

IS THIS THE ABODE OF MR. HYDE?

VERY WELL THEN, WE WISH TO SEE HIS ROOMS. I AM INSPECTOR NEWCOMEN OF SCOTLAND YARD.

YES, BUT HE'S NOT HERE. HE CAME IN VERY LATE AND LEFT AGAIN WITHIN THE HOUR.

HIS HABITS ARE *VERY* IRREGULAR.

AH! HE IS IN TROUBLE! WHAT HAS HE *DONE*?

HE DOESN'T SEEM A VERY *POPULAR* CHARACTER.

Chapter Six

IT WAS LATE IN THE AFTERNOON WHEN MR. UTTERSON FOUND HIS WAY TO DR. JEKYLL'S DOOR...

CAREW WAS MY CLIENT, BUT SO ARE YOU, AND I WANT TO KNOW WHAT IS GOING ON. YOU HAVE NOT BEEN MAD ENOUGH TO HIDE THIS FELLOW?

... AND INDEED HE DOES NOT WANT MY HELP; YOU DO NOT KNOW HIM AS I DO.

UTTERSON, I SWEAR TO GOD, I WILL NEVER SET EYES ON HIM AGAIN. I AM DONE WITH HIM IN THIS WORLD. IT IS ALL AT AN END...

YOU SEEM PRETTY SURE OF HIM, AND FOR YOUR SAKE, I HOPE YOU MAY BE RIGHT. IF IT CAME TO TRIAL, YOUR NAME MIGHT APPEAR.

I AM QUITE SURE OF HIM. I HAVE GROUNDS FOR CERTAINTY THAT I CANNOT SHARE WITH ANYONE...

... I HAVE RECEIVED A LETTER, DELIVERED HERE BY HAND TODAY, AND I AM AT A LOSS WHETHER I SHOULD SHOW IT TO THE POLICE...

... BUT THERE IS ONE THING ON WHICH YOU MAY ADVISE ME...

... I SHOULD LIKE TO LEAVE IT IN YOUR HANDS. I HAVE SO GREAT TRUST IN YOU.

YOU FEAR, I SUPPOSE, THAT IT MIGHT LEAD TO HIS DETECTION?

NO, I CANNOT SAY THAT I CARE WHAT BECOMES OF HYDE. I WAS THINKING OF MY OWN CHARACTER, WHICH THIS HATEFUL BUSINESS HAS RATHER EXPOSED.

WELL, LET ME SEE THE LETTER.

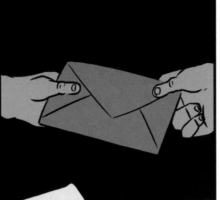

To me benefactor, Dr. Jekyll,

You need labor under no alarm for my safety. I have means of escape on which i may place a sure dependence.

yours,

Edward Hyde

SHALL I KEEP THIS AND SLEEP UPON IT?

I WISH YOU TO JUDGE FOR ME ENTIRELY. I HAVE LOST CONFIDENCE IN MYSELF.

VERY WELL. ONE MORE THING. WAS IT HYDE WHO DICTATED THE TERMS IN YOUR WILL ABOUT YOUR DISAPPEARANCE?

IT WAS.

I KNEW IT. HE MEANT TO MURDER YOU. YOU HAVE HAD A FINE ESCAPE.

I HAVE HAD WHAT IS FAR MORE TO THE PURPOSE--A LESSON. OH GOD, WHAT A LESSON I HAVE HAD!

MESSRS. MAW WHOLESALE CHEMISTS

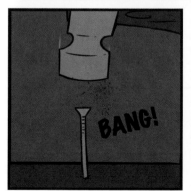

BANG!

BANG!

BANG!

SLAM!

CLICK!

CRUNCH!

HYDE IS HENCEFORTH IMPOSSIBLE!
WHETHER I WANT TO OR NOT, I MUST
NOW CONFINE MYSELF TO THE BETTER
PART OF MY EXISTENCE!

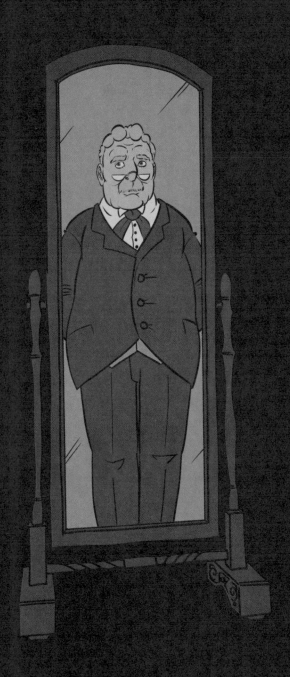

Chapter Seven

IT HAD BEEN SOME TIME SINCE
JEKYLL HAD INVITED HIS FRIENDS
OVER FOR ONE OF HIS FAMOUS
DINNERS...

WE HAVE NOT SEEN YOU MUCH OF LATE, JEKYLL.

INDEED, I HAVE BEEN KEPT VERY BUSY WITH MY LATEST PROJECT-- RENOVATING OUR PARISH CHURCH.

SO I HEAR. SUCH WORKS MUST DO YOU THE WEALTH OF GOOD--YOU ARE THE PICTURE OF FINE HEALTH.

THE NEXT MORNING, FILLED WITH AN ENORMOUS SENSE OF WELL-BEING AND SATISFACTION, DR. JEKYLL TOOK A RELAXED STROLL THROUGH REGENT'S PARK.

YES, AFTER ALL, I AM QUITE LIKE THEM—AN UPSTANDING MEMBER OF SOCIETY. FOR THE REST OF MY LIFE I WILL DO GOOD WORKS, AND REDEEM MY PAST.

NO! IT CANNOT BE!

My dear friend Lanyon,
I must ask you an urgent favor.
Go to my house and take from
my laboratory desk the sample
I have recently been working
on. Poole will be able to
show you where it is. Take it
immediately to the address on
the envelope. My associate will
explain all when you arrive.
Yours in haste,
Jekyll

ON RECEIPT OF THE TELEGRAM, LANYON FOLLOWED THE INSTRUCTIONS WITH HASTE.

RAT-TAT-TAT.

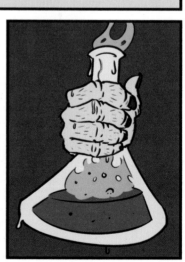

AND NOW, WILL YOU LEAVE ME WITH THIS VIAL IN MY HAND AND GO FORTH FROM THIS HOUSE NONE THE WISER...

... OR HAS THE GREED OF CURIOSITY TOO MUCH COMMAND OF YOU? IT SHALL BE DONE AS YOU DECIDE...

... BUT KNOW THAT IF YOU STAY TO WATCH, A NEW PROVINCE OF KNOWLEDGE AND NEW AVENUES TO FAME SHALL BE LAID UPON YOU.

I HAVE GONE TOO FAR IN THE WAY OF INEXPLICABLE SERVICES TO PAUSE BEFORE I SEE THE END.

IT IS WELL. DR. LANYON, REMEMBER YOUR VOWS. WHAT FOLLOWS IS UNDER THE SEAL OF YOUR PROFESSION. BEHOLD!

JEKYLL FLED LANCOME'S HOUSE WITHOUT ANOTHER WORD AND WENT STRAIGHT HOME.

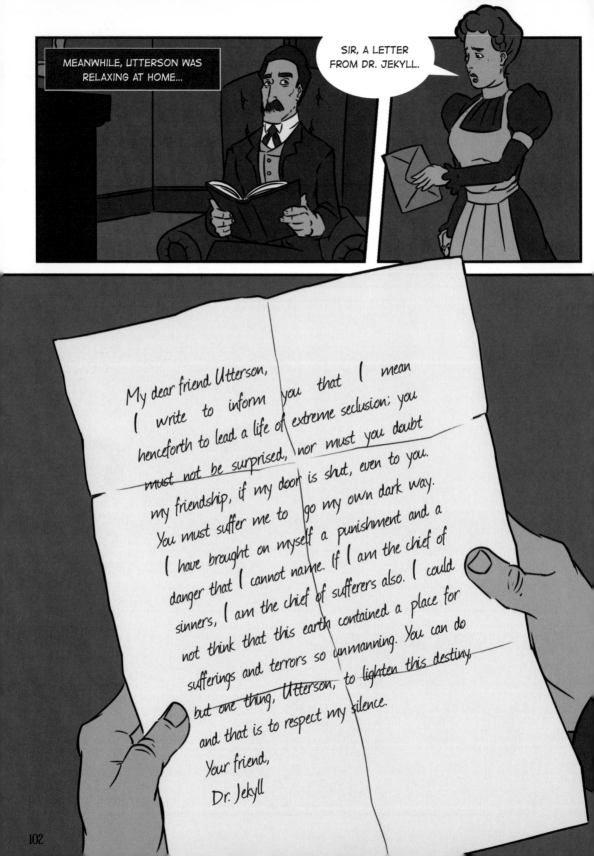

MY DEAR FRIEND, ARE
YOU QUITE WELL?

Chapter Eight

A WEEK LATER, UTTERSON RECEIVED THE SAD NEWS THAT LANYON HAD PASSED AWAY.

BLESS GOD! IT'S MR. UTTERSON.

THEY'RE ALL AFRAID.

FETCH ME A CANDLE.

THIS IS UNQUESTIONABLY THE DOCTOR'S HAND?

WHAT DOES THE HANDWRITING MATTER? I HAVE SEEN HIM!

SEEN HIM?

IT SEEMS HE HAD SLIPPED OUT TO LOOK FOR THIS DRUG, OR WHATEVER IT IS. HE WAS DIGGING ABOUT IN ONE OF THOSE CRATES. HE LOOKED UP WHEN I CAME IN, GAVE A KIND OF CRY, AND WHIPPED BACK INTO THE ROOM. THAT THING WAS NOT MY MASTER, AND THERE'S THE TRUTH. MY MASTER IS A TALL FINE BUILD OF A MAN, AND THIS WAS MORE OF A DWARF. AND I BELIEVE MURDER TO HAVE BEEN DONE!

THEN IT IS OUR DUTY TO MAKE CERTAIN!

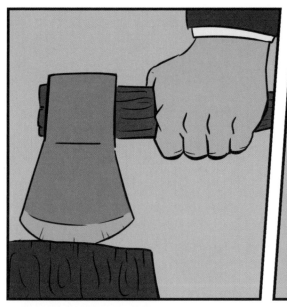

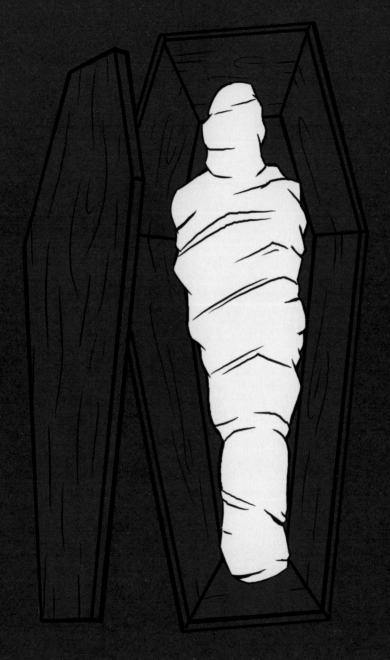

The Body Snatcher

LATER THAT NIGHT...

KNOCK! KNOCK!

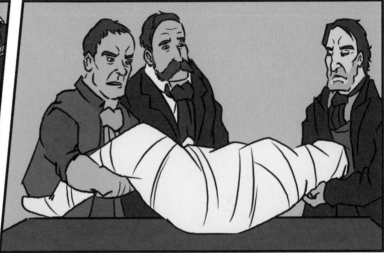

NOVEMBER 1828, THE
STAR AND GARTER.

I'LL HAVE ANOTHER, GOOD MAN. FOR THIS DAMN'D TOOTHACHE.

AYE, I SUSPECTED AS MUCH, MR. FETTES.

GOOD DAY, MISS GALBRAITH.

GOOD DAY, MR. FETTES.

LATER.

KNOCK
KNOCK

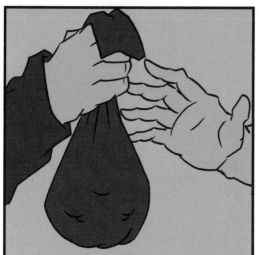

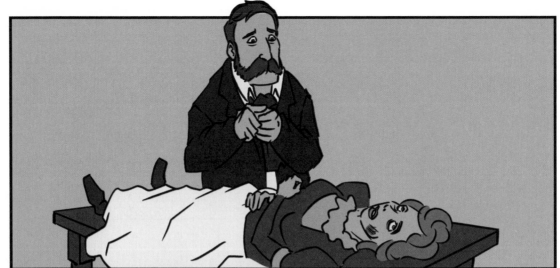

THE NEXT MORNING.

HOW GOES IT, FETTES?

MACFARLANE, I'M GLAD YOU'RE HERE. SOMETHING TERRIBLE HAS HAPPENED. LOOK--

AYE, YES. IT DOES SEEM A LITTLE FISHY.

WELL, WHAT SHOULD I DO?

DO? DO YOU WANT TO DO ANYTHING? LEAST SAID, SOONEST MENDED, I SHOULD SAY.

BUT SOMEONE ELSE MIGHT RECOGNIZE HER. SHE WAS WELL-KNOWN AND POPULAR.

WELL, LET'S HOPE NOT. AND IF ANYBODY DOES, THEN YOU DIDN'T. THE FACT IS, THIS HAS BEEN GOING ON TOO LONG. STIR UP THE MUD AND YOU'LL GET KING IN THE MOST UNHOLY TROUBLE.

MACFARLANE!

OH, HUSH. I SHOULD LIKE TO KNOW HOW ANY ONE OF US WOULD LOOK IN A WITNESS BOX. FOR ME, YOU KNOW THERE'S ONE THING THAT'S CERTAIN-- PRACTICALLY SPEAKING, ALL OUR SUBJECTS HAVE BEEN MURDERED.

SUSPECTING IS ONE THING AND--

AND PROOF ANOTHER. YES, I KNOW. AND I'M AS SORRY AS YOU ARE THAT THIS SHOULD HAVE COME HERE. BUT THE NEXT BEST THING FOR ME IS NOT TO RECOGNIZE IT, AND I THINK A MAN OF THE WORLD WOULD DO AS I DO.

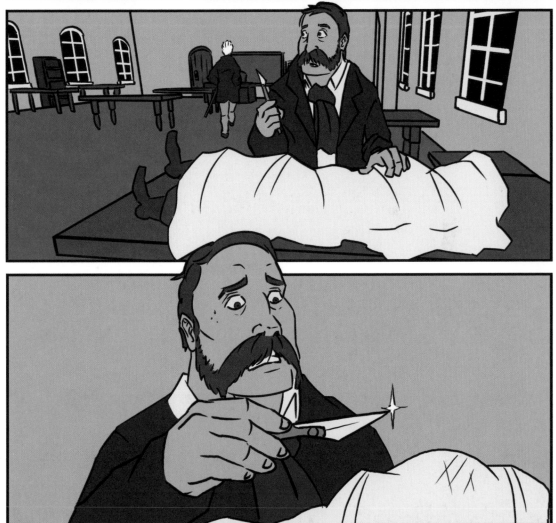

DECEMBER 1828, THE STAR AND GARTER.

GOOD AFTERNOON, MACFARLANE.

I DON'T BELIEVE WE'VE BEEN INTRODUCED, MISTER--?

GRAY, GOOD SIR. YOU MUST BE FETTES.

AYE.

I'VE HEARD ALL ABOUT YOU FROM TODDY, HERE.

DON'T YOU CALL ME THAT CONFOUNDED NAME!

STOP YOUR INCESSANT WHINING, AND FETCH YOUR FRIEND A GLASS.

I'VE HEARD GREAT THINGS ABOUT YOU, FETTES. TODDY SPEAKS QUITE HIGHLY OF YOUR WORK.

HE DOES?

AND I KNOW HOW TO SPOT AN EAGER FELLOW LIKE YOURSELF.

WHEN YOU'RE NEXT IN LONDON, BE SURE TO CALL ON ME. I AM VERY WELL-CONNECTED, AND I'M SURE I COULD BE OF SOME USE TO YOU.

PLYING FETTES WITH DRINKS AND PROSPECTS ARE YOU, MR. GRAY?

WELL, THERE IS NO NEED TO BE JEALOUS, TODDY.

I HAVE ASKED YOU REPEATEDLY...

HEAR HIM! DID YOU EVER SEE THE LADS PLAY KNIFE? HE WOULD LIKE TO DO THAT ALL OVER MY BODY!

WE MEDICALS HAVE A BETTER WAY THAN THAT. WHEN WE DISLIKE A DEAR FRIEND OF OURS, WE DISSECT HIM.

HA! HA!

COME, LET'S GO TO DINNER. YOU WILL JOIN US, MR. FETTES, I INSIST.

TODDY, BE A GOOD MAN AND FETCH US SOME MORE WINE.

THE FOLLOWING NIGHT.

KNOCK — KNOCK!

MACFARLANE! WHAT A SURPRISE. DID YOU SUFFER AS MUCH AS I DID TODAY? MY HEADACHE HAS ONLY JUST BEGUN TO SUBSIDE.

GOOD HEAVENS! WHEREVER DID YOU...? WHAT HAPPENED TO THE OTHER TWO WHO NORMALLY BRING THE BODIES? HOW DID YOU MANAGE ALONE?

STOP RABBITING ON AND HELP ME WITH HIM, WON'T YOU?

BUT WHERE, AND HOW, AND WHEN DID YOU COME BY IT?

YOU'D BETTER LOOK AT THE FACE.

I HAVE PUT MY NECK IN A HALTER TO OBLIGE YOU, SIR.

TO OBLIGE *ME?* YOU DID WHAT HAD TO BE DONE. MR. GRAY IS THE CONTINUATION OF MISS GALBRAITH. YOU CAN'T BEGIN AND THEN STOP. THAT'S THE TRUTH. NO REST FOR THE WICKED.

MY GOD! WHAT HAVE I DONE?

MY DEAR FELLOW. I LIKE YOU, AND KING LIKES YOU. YOU WERE BORN TO LEAD THE HUNT. AND I TELL YOU, ON MY HONOR AND MY EXPERIENCE OF LIFE, IN THREE DAYS YOU'LL LAUGH AT ALL THESE SCARECROWS LIKE A SCHOOLBOY AT A FARCE.

NOW GET TO WORK.

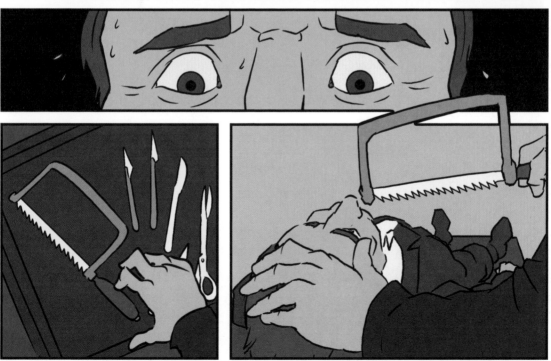

THREE DAYS LATER, SOMEWHERE OUTSIDE THE CITY.

DO NOT SPEAK OF IT, MAN. HERE IS A COMPLIMENT BETWEEN FRIENDS.

MACFARLANE... WITH REGARDS TO THE OTHER DAY... I...

I WAS AN ASS TILL I KNEW YOU. YOU AND KING, BY THE LORD, HARRY, YOU'LL MAKE A MAN OF ME!

IT TOOK A MAN TO BACK ME UP THE OTHER MORNING. THERE ARE SOME BIG, BRAWLING COWARDS WHO WOULD HAVE TURNED SICK AT THE SIGHT OF THAT THING; BUT NOT YOU--YOU KEPT YOUR HEAD.

AND WHY NOT? THERE WAS NOTHING TO GAIN ON THE ONE SIDE BUT DISTURBANCE, AND ON THE OTHER I COULD COUNT ON YOUR GRATITUDE, DON'T YOU SEE?

I THINK WE'RE READY TO LIFT THIS OUT.

BANG!

WHAT WOULD HER HUSBAND THINK, EH? OUT LATE AT NIGHT WITH TWO MEN!

THAT IS NOT A WOMAN.

IT WAS A WOMAN WHEN WE PUT HER IN.

HOLD THAT LAMP--I MUST SEE THE FACE.

Acknowledgments

I'd like to thank Jess for putting up with me both when it was going well (The Jekyll Times) and when I wanted to throw my computer out of the window (The Hyde Times). Thanks to Sarah Herman and Lyndsey Harwood (it wouldn't have happened without you), to Danny West for his advice in the early stages (he reads a lot of comics), and of course to Lucy York and Chris Turton for giving me the opportunity to realize my dream of drawing and coloring in for money and making the process as painless as possible!